Five Concertos

Johann Sebastian Bach.

Kevin Mayhew

Extracted from

The Complete Organ Works of J S Bach

Executive Editor Alan Ridout
Managing Editor Anthea Smith
Music Setting Christopher Hinkins

This compilation first published in Great Britain in 1995 by
KEVIN MAYHEW LTD
Rattlesden
Bury St Edmunds
Suffolk IP30 0SZ

ISBN 0 86209 630 8
Catalogue No: 1400047

Printed and bound in Hong Kong

Contents

Concerto in G after Johann Ernst

* *These appear as Oberwerk (I) and Rückpositiv (II) in the earliest source.*

I
I
tr
II
II
I
I
tr
tr
II
II

II

* These appear as Oberwerk (I) and Rückpositiv (II) in the earliest source.

III

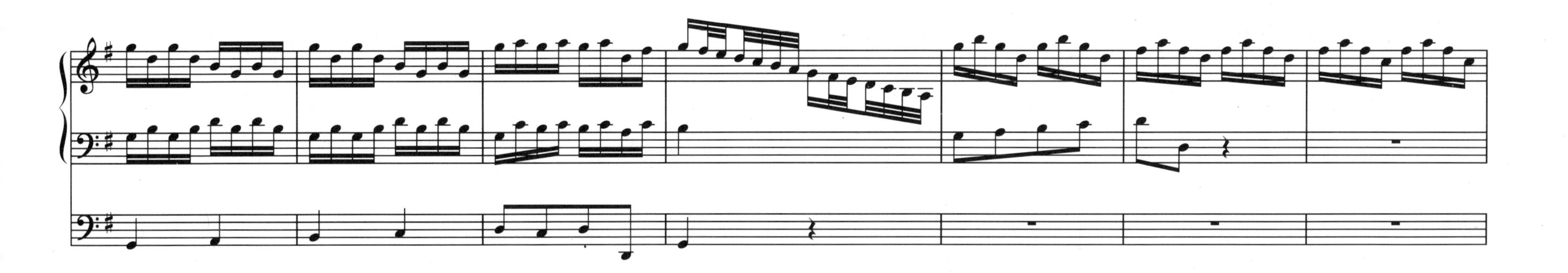

Concerto in C after Antonio Vivaldi

I

BWV 594

* *These appear as Oberwerk (I) and Rückpositiv (II) in the earliest source.*

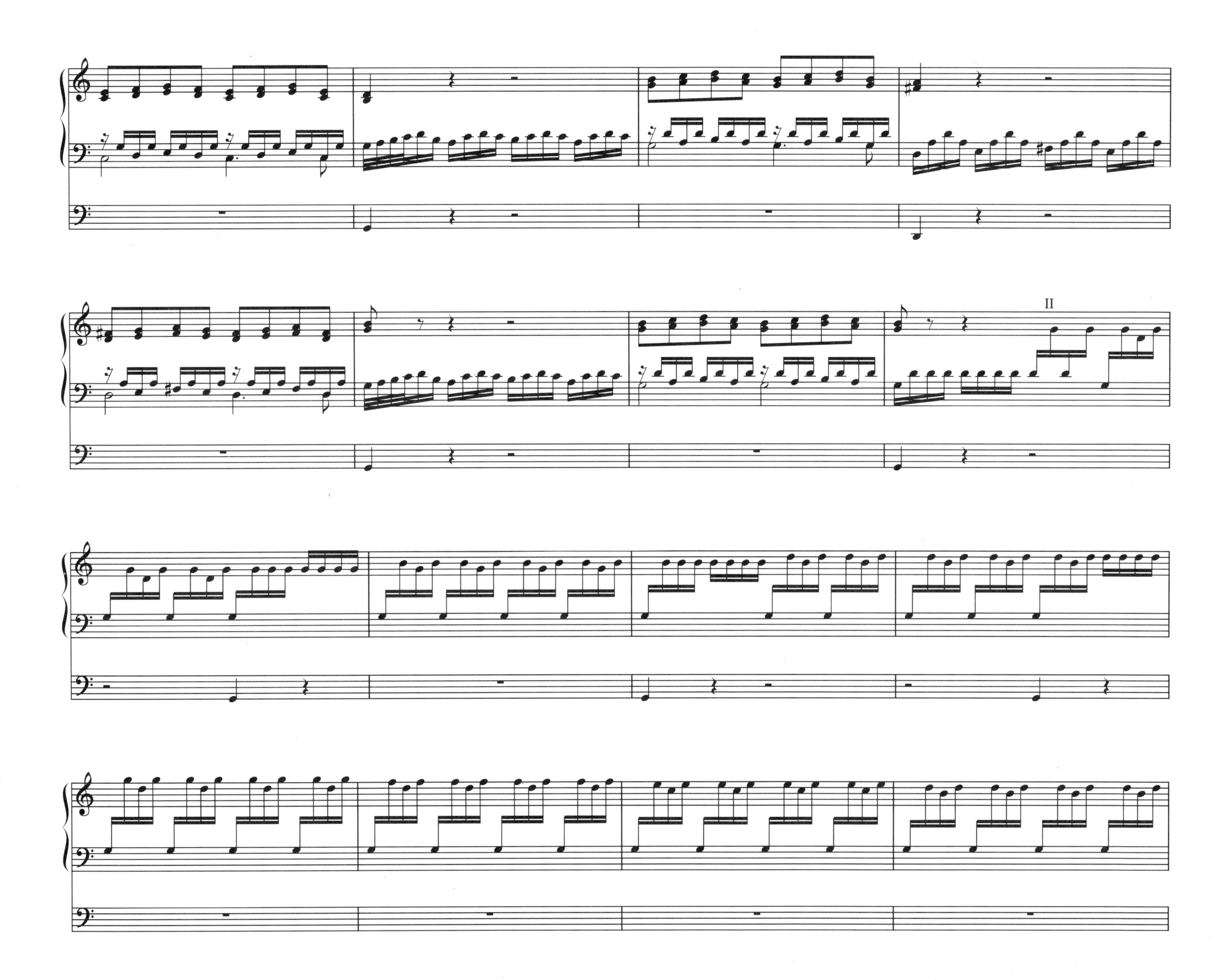
II

I
I
I
II

I

II
I
II

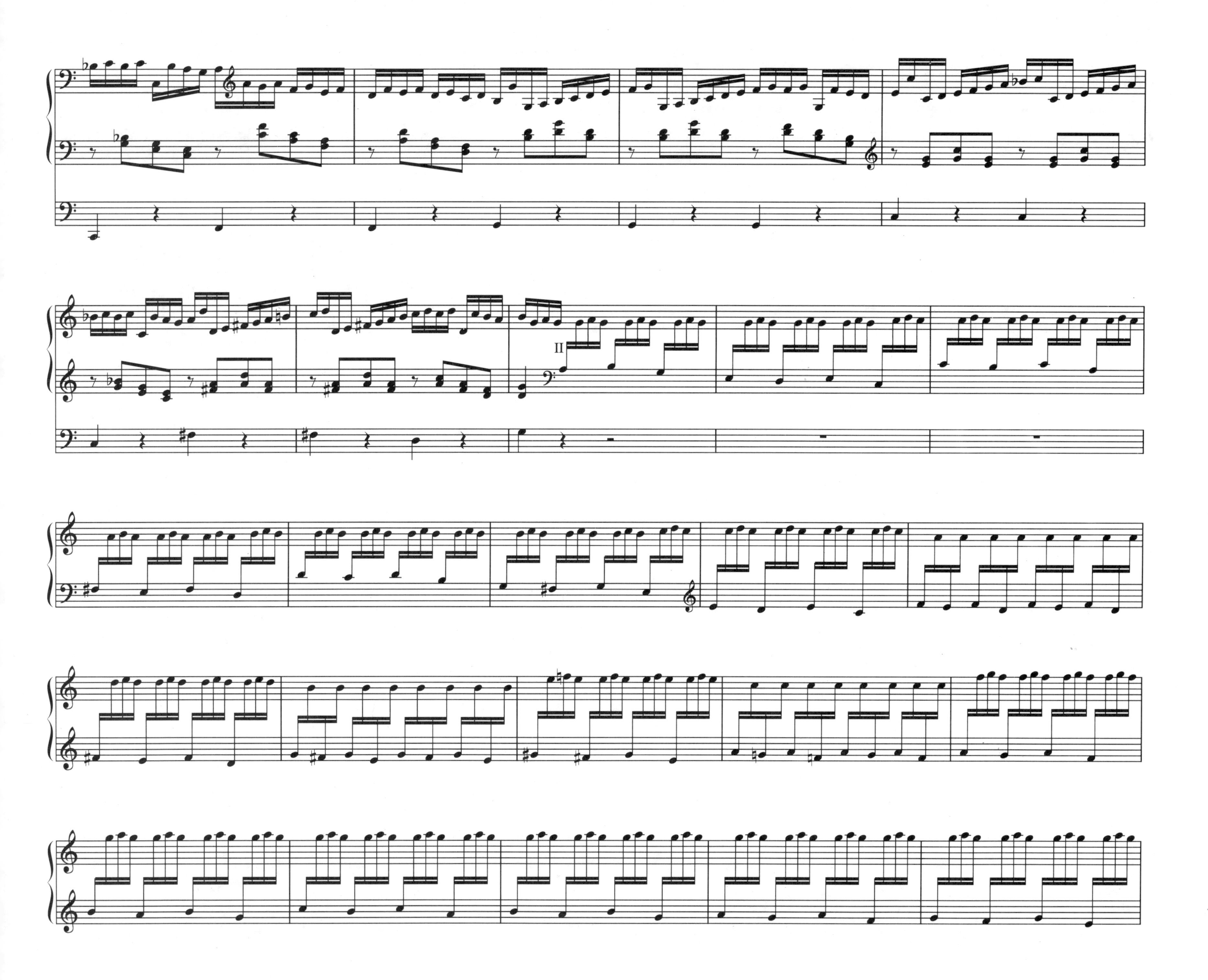
II

tr
I
I

II Recitativo

* These appear as Oberwerk (I) and Rückpositiv (II) in the earliest source.

tr
3

III

* These appear as Oberwerk (I) and Rückpositiv (II) in the earliest source.

tr
I
II

II
I
II
I

I
II
tr
sim.
II

tr
tr
tr
I
I
II Solo

tr
sim.
3

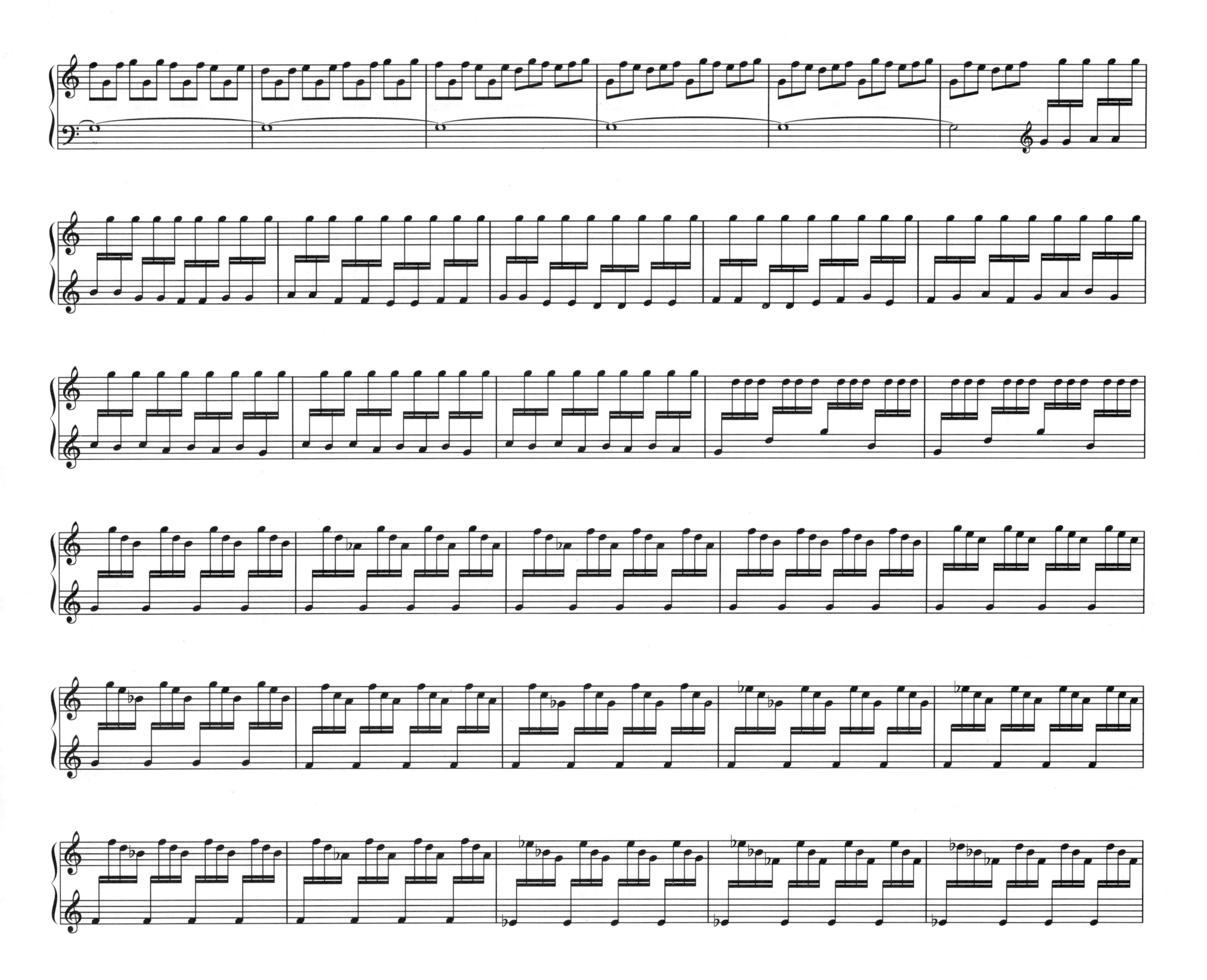

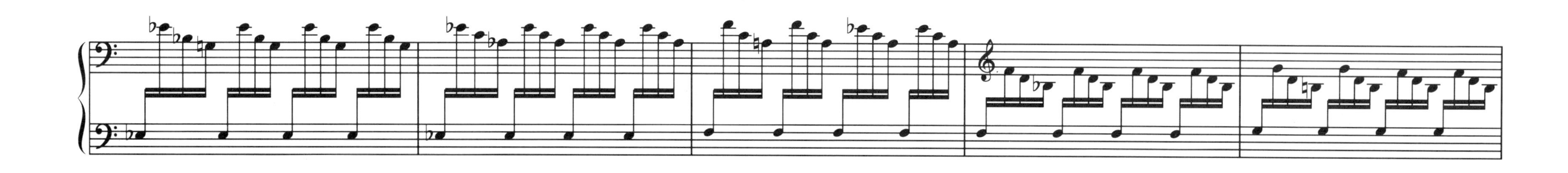

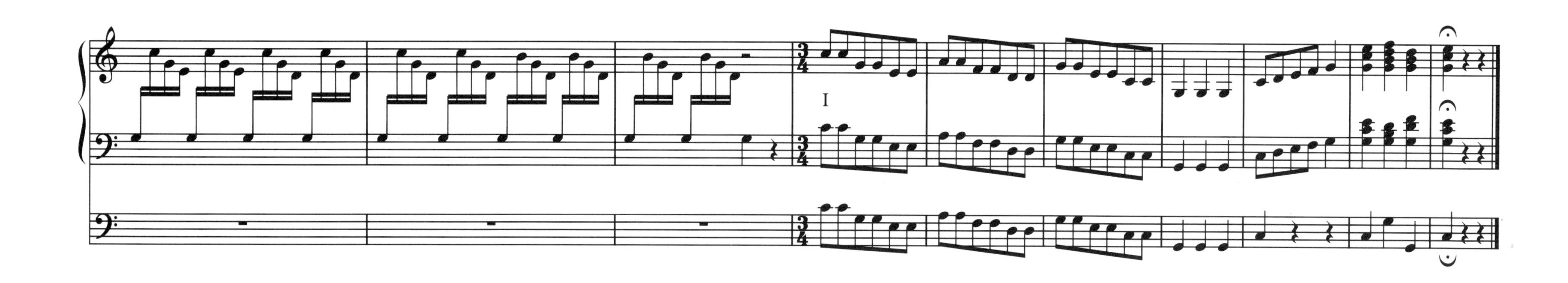
I

Concerto in A minor after Antonio Vivaldi

I

BWV 593

* *These appear as Oberwerk (I) and Rückpositiv (II) in the earliest source.*

II
I
II
II
I
I

(I)
II
Organo
pleno
II

I
I
II
II
I
I
II

I
II
I

II

III

* *These appear as Oberwerk (I) and Rückpositiv (II) in the earliest source.*

I
II

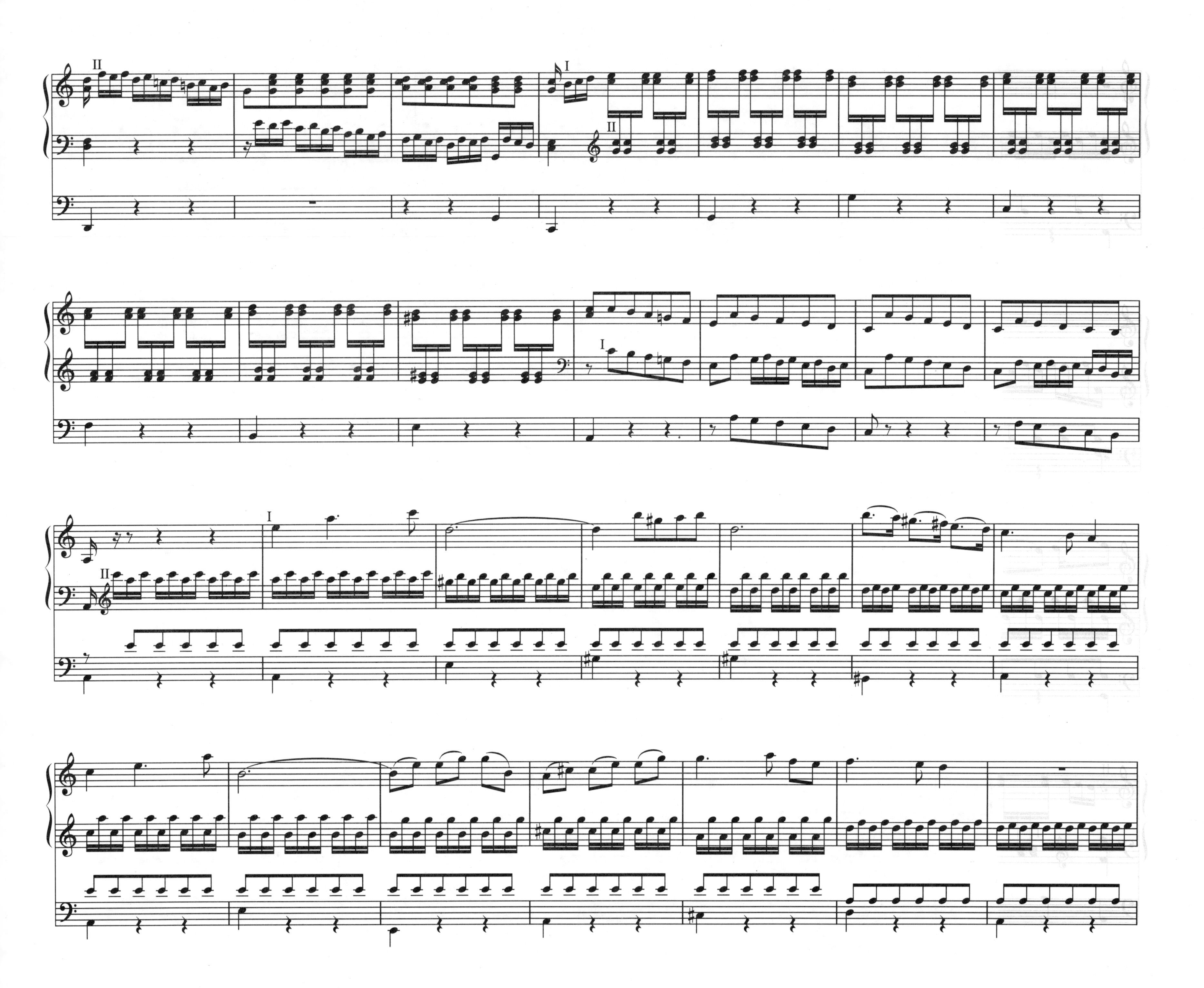
II
I
II
I
II
I

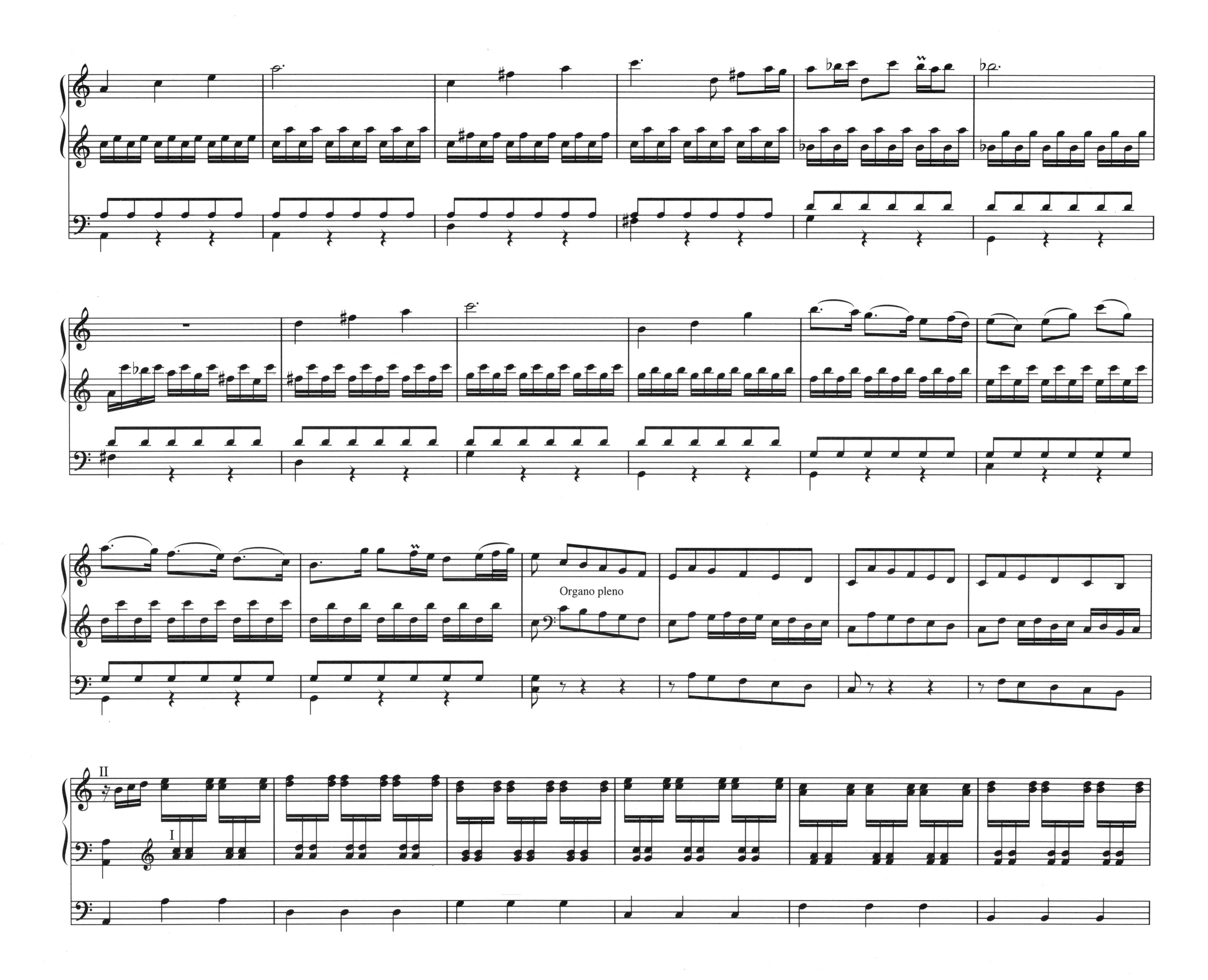
Organo pleno
II
I

I
II
I

Concerto in D minor after Antonio Vivaldi

I

BWV 596

* *These appear as Oberwerk (I) and Brustpositiv (III) in the earliest source.*

III
I Principal 8´ + Octava 4´
Subbaß 32´
II
Grave
Pleno

III Fugue

Johann Sebastian Bach

IV

V

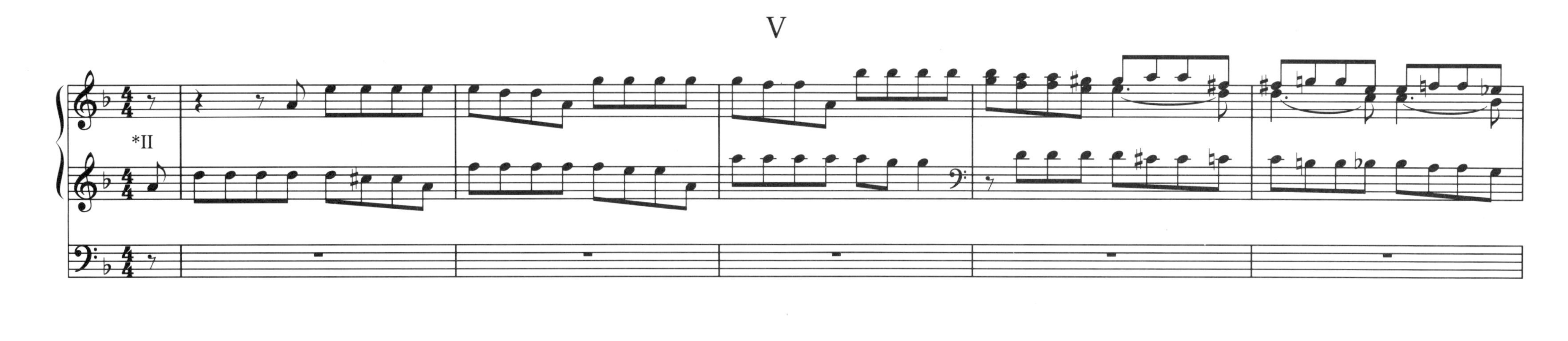

* *These appear as Oberwerk (I) and Rückpositiv (II) in the earliest source.*

I

II
I
II
II
I
II
I
II

I
I

Concerto in C after Johann Ernst

* *These appear as Oberwerk (I) and Rückpositiv (II) in the earliest source.*

I
II
tr

II
I
II

66
I
II
I
II
I

70

74
II
I
II
I
II
I
II
I

78

Ornamentation

J S Bach himself left one indicator on ornamentation in the form of a table of thirteen ornaments and their written-out equivalents for his ten-year-old son, Wilhelm Friedemann. It is given here without the brief verbal descriptions which in many cases are now either obsolete or actually misleading.

It is tempting to exaggerate the importance of this list coming, as it does, from the hand of the master and for an instructional purpose. There are problems to it as it is applied to specific music; and it is not comprehensive. Yet to focus too assiduously on the problems is probably to underestimate its importance. So long as it is taken as a general guide and not as an infallible statement it will prove very useful.

ALAN RIDOUT

'Explanation of various signs, showing how to play certain ornaments neatly'

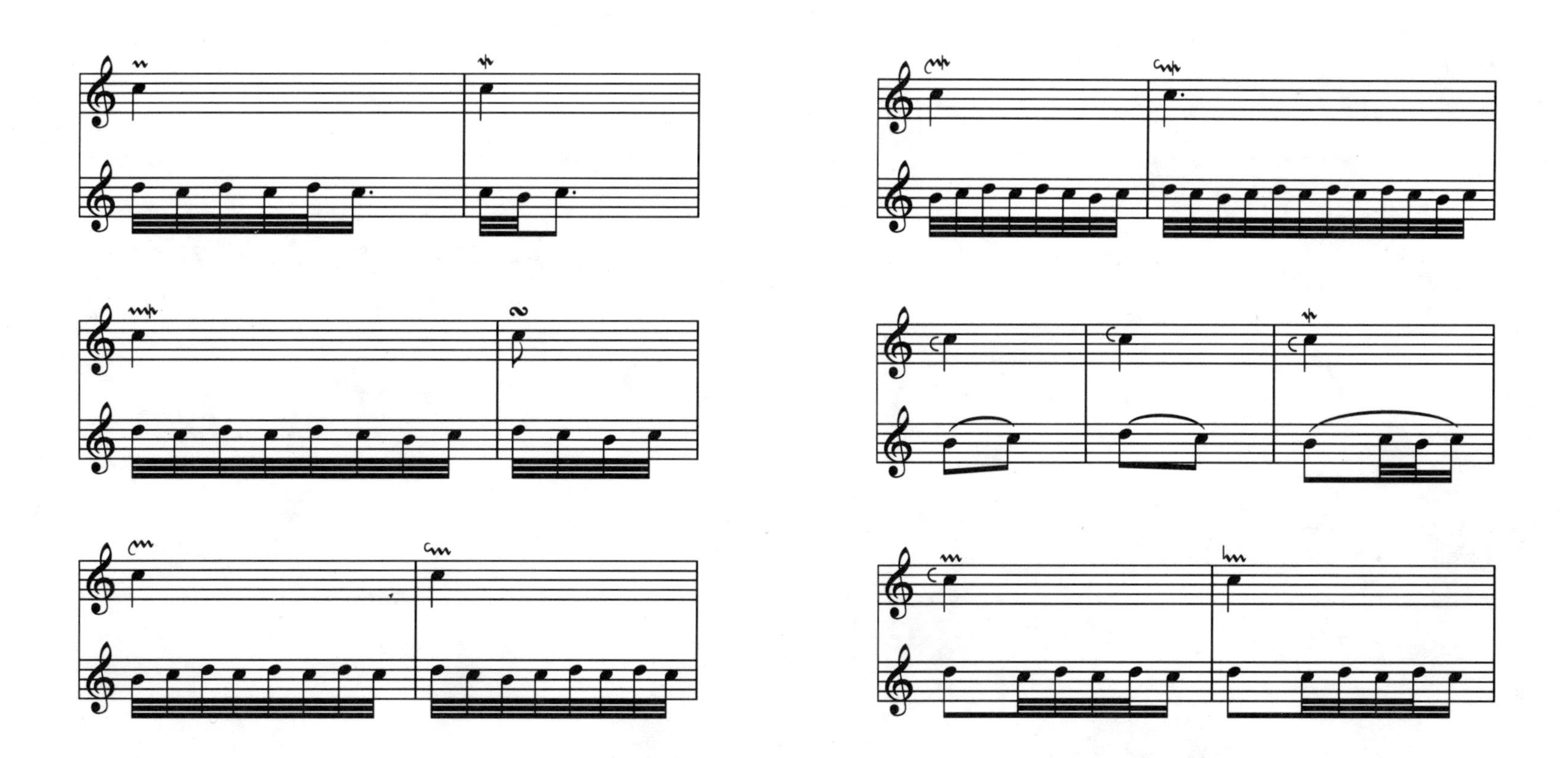